Usborne English Reader
Level 1

Cinderella

Retold by Laura Cowan
Illustrated by Sara Gianassi

English language consultant: Peter Viney

Contents

You can listen to the story online here:
www.usborneenglishreaders.com/
cinderella

Isabella lived in a big house in the city. Her mother died when she was very young, and her father was often away from home. Isabella was sad when he was away. The servants were kind, but she was alone all day.

One day,
her father married again.
"Isabella, my dear, this is your new
stepmother," he said. Her stepmother had
two daughters, Griselda and Imelda. Isabella
was much prettier and nicer than Griselda and
Imelda, and her stepmother hated her.

Two years later, Isabella's father died. Her stepmother sent all the servants away. "Isabella, you can do their work," she said.

Isabella liked helping people, so she didn't complain. Her stepmother said, "You can sleep on the kitchen floor by the fire. Then you can start work when you wake up." The floor was dirty with cinders from the fire. Griselda said, "Look at Isabella in the cinders! Let's call her Cinder-ella."

"Take my shoes, Cinderella!" "Bring my dress, Cinderella!" They were always shouting. There was a lot of work, but Cinderella smiled and never complained.

The stepsisters wore beautiful dresses. They went to parties and ate the nicest food. Cinderella's clothes were old and dirty, and she stayed at home and ate bread and water.

One day, there was a knock at the door. It was a servant from the palace. "Ladies, I have an invitation for you," he said. "There is going to be a ball at the palace tomorrow night. The Prince wants to get married. He would like to meet every lady in the city."

Cinderella's stepmother took the invitation. "Oh, my girls love parties!" She didn't say thank you.

The stepsisters were excited. "I'm going to wear my new blue dress, Griselda!"

"But I want to wear *my* blue dress, Imelda!"

"I'm going to marry the Prince!"

"Ha! The Prince isn't going to look at *you*!"

"Please, can I wear one of your old dresses?" Cinderella asked.

They all laughed at her. "*You* can't go," said her stepmother. "Look at you!"

"Even our old clothes are too nice for you!" said Griselda.

The next evening, Cinderella's stepmother and sisters went to the ball. Cinderella sat in the kitchen, alone. It was very quiet. There was a big orange pumpkin on the table for dinner the next day. A mouse ran over her foot, and then another. She started to cry.

Suddenly the kitchen was full of light. Cinderella saw an old lady with a magic wand. Cinderella was frightened, but the old lady smiled kindly.

"Who are you?" asked Cinderella.

"My dear, I'm your fairy godmother. Why are you crying?"

"Because everyone in the city is at the Prince's ball, but I can't go."

"Don't worry, Cinderella, you shall go to the ball."

"But I'm so dirty, and I don't have any nice dresses." Suddenly her old clothes changed into a gold and silver ball dress. Cinderella looked down at her feet. She was wearing glass slippers, the prettiest shoes in the world.

Cinderella smiled. "Oh, thank you!"

"Come outside, my dear," said the fairy. She put the pumpkin and four mice on the ground, and touched them with her wand. The pumpkin changed into a gold and silver coach, and the mice were four white horses.

"They're beautiful!" said Cinderella.

"We need a coachman," said the fairy. "Where's your stepmother's little dog?"

The dog ran out of the house. The fairy touched him with her wand, and he changed into a coachman.

"Thank you so much! I really can go to the ball!"

"Wait, my dear, this is very important," said the fairy. "You must come home before twelve o'clock. At midnight, my magic ends."

When Cinderella walked into the
ballroom, in her beautiful dress,
everyone stopped talking. Even the music
stopped.

"Who is she?" Griselda whispered to
Imelda. "She's so beautiful."

"Is she a princess?" Imelda whispered
back. "Look at her slippers!"

Cinderella was a little frightened. She stood alone by the door and looked down at the floor. Suddenly a servant was standing next to her.

"My lady, the Prince would like to dance with you."

Cinderella looked up and saw the handsomest man in the world. He was smiling at her. After one dance, the Prince asked her for another, and then another. They danced for hours.

Then Cinderella heard the palace clock. *DONG! DONG! DONG! DONG!..*

"Oh no!" she said. "It's midnight! I must go."

"But I don't know your name," said the Prince. It was too late! Cinderella ran out of the palace. Her beautiful dress was old and dirty again. The gold and silver coach changed into a pumpkin, the horses were mice and the coachman was a little dog.

Nobody can run fast in glass slippers. Cinderella fell down near the palace and lost one. She stood up, picked up the other slipper and ran all the way home.

The Prince ran after her, but Cinderella was gone. On the ground near the palace, he saw a glass slipper.

The next morning, everyone in the city was talking about the beautiful stranger. Everyone in Cinderella's house was talking, too.

"Who is she?" said Griselda. "Nobody knows. She ran out of the ballroom at midnight. They just found her glass slipper."

"Every woman in the city must try the slipper. The Prince says so," Imelda told her mother.

Later that day, there was a knock at the door. "The Prince is here!" shouted Griselda.

Upstairs, Cinderella put her hands over her ears. "What can I do?" she thought. The Prince had her slipper, but now she was dirty and so were her clothes. She didn't want the Prince to see her.

The Prince came into the house with his servants. One servant was holding the glass slipper.

"Good afternoon, ladies," said a servant. "Can you help us?"

"Yes, of course!" Imelda ran forward. "Let me try first." She sat down with the slipper, but her foot was too wide.

Griselda laughed at her sister. She tried the slipper, but her foot was too long.

Cinderella came slowly down the stairs. "Please, can I try?" she asked.

"Yes, of course you can," said the Prince. He looked at her carefully. "Do I know you?"

"Ha, that's Cinderella. No one knows *her*!" said Griselda.

"She's not important," said Imelda.

"Be quiet," said the Prince. "Please, come here, Cinderella."

Cinderella sat down and tried the slipper. It was exactly the right size. She took the other slipper from the pocket of her dress, and put it on her other foot.

Suddenly, the room was full of light, and Cinderella's fairy godmother was there. She touched Cinderella with her wand, and the cinders were gone. She was wearing a ball dress. She looked even more beautiful than before.

"I knew it!" said the Prince. "It was you, at the ball!"

"What?" shouted Cinderella's stepmother. "*Cinderella*? What about my Griselda or Imelda?"

The Prince didn't listen. He took Cinderella's hand.

"Cinderella isn't my real name," said Cinderella quietly. "It's Isabella."

"Isabella or Cinderella, you're the most beautiful woman in the city, and the nicest too. Please, marry me," said the Prince. Cinderella held his hand, closed her eyes and smiled.

About the story

Charles Perrault lived in France from 1628-1703. For most of his life, he worked for the French government, but he was always very interested in books and stories too. In 1695, Perrault lost his government job and started writing stories for his children. *Cinderella* is one of these stories. Perrault took the idea from a much older story, but he added the fairy godmother and the glass slippers.

Perrault's stories were soon very popular, not only in France but all over Europe too. Today, people know and love these stories all around the world. This kind of story is called a fairy story. Fairy stories are often about kings, queens, princes and princesses, fairies and magic. Other fairy stories by Perrault include *Little Red Riding Hood*, *Sleeping Beauty* and *Puss in Boots*.

Activities

The answers are on page 32.

What happened when?

Can you put these pictures in the right order?

A.

"Every woman in the city must try the slipper."

B.

"It was you, at the ball!"

C.

"There is going to be a ball at the palace tomorrow night."

D.

Cinderella ran out of the palace.

E.

"Don't worry, Cinderella, you shall go to the ball."

F.

"My lady, the Prince would like to dance with you."

What do they want?

Choose the right sentence for each person.

A.
I want to wear my new blue dress.

B.
But I want to wear *my* blue dress, Imelda!

C.
I want to go to the ball.

D.
I want to find the beautiful stranger.

E.
I want to help Cinderella.

Griselda

Prince

Imelda

Cinderella

Fairy Godmother

What do they think? How do they feel?

Choose the right word to finish each sentence.

sad	dirty	excited	kind	quiet
important		handsome		frightened

1.

Isabella was .... when her father was away.

2.

The stepsisters were ....

3.

Cinderella was a little ....

4.

"She's not ....," said Imelda.

You shall go to the ball

The Fairy Godmother touched all the things on the left with her wand. What did they change into?

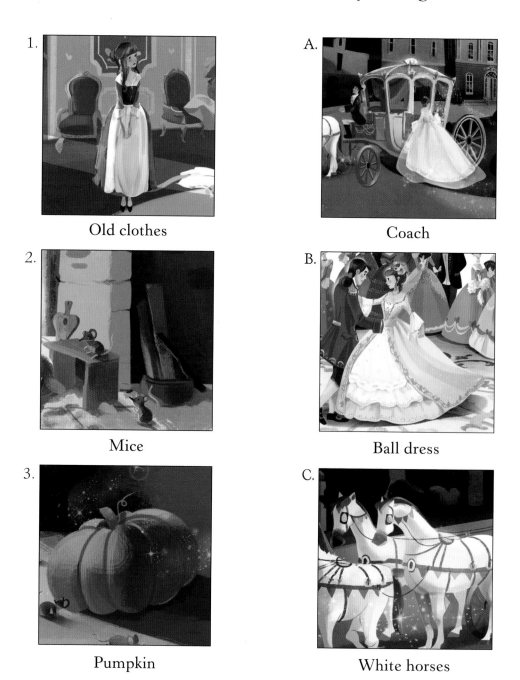

1. Old clothes

A. Coach

2. Mice

B. Ball dress

3. Pumpkin

C. White horses

What happened next?

Choose the right sentence.

1. Cinderella sat in the kitchen, alone.

   A. Suddenly the kitchen was full of light.

   B. Suddenly the kitchen was full of mice.

2. The Prince ran after her, but Cinderella was gone.

   A. On the ground near the palace he saw a pumpkin.

   B. On the ground near the palace he saw a glass slipper.

3. Cinderella's fairy godmother was there.

   A. She touched Cinderella with her wand, and the cinders were gone.

   B. She touched Cinderella with her wand, and the sisters were gone.

Word list

alone (adj) without other people.

another (det) one more.

ball (n) a very grand formal party, with dancing.

cinders (n pl) small black, burned pieces from a fire.

coach (n) something that you ride in. In the past, coaches were pulled by horses.

complain (v) when you are not happy about something and you say so, you complain.

dear (n) you say "my dear" to someone you like very much or love.

exactly (adv) no more and no less.

glass (n) a hard material that you can see through. Windows are made of glass.

godmother (n) a woman who is not in your family, but who promises to help you when you are growing up.

gone (adj) not there any more.

handsome (adj) (*about a man*) good-looking.

hate (v) when you really don't like someone and you want bad things to happen to them, you hate them.

invitation (n) a way of asking someone to a party or other event. An invitation can be a letter, or something you say.

knock (n) the sound that you make when you tap a door to tell people you are there.

lady (n) a polite word for a woman.

midnight (n) twelve o'clock at night.

pocket (n) pockets in your clothes are places where you can keep money or other things that you need to have with you.

pumpkin (n) a large round orange vegetable.

servant (n) someone who works for another person, especially in their home.

size (n) how big or small something is.

slipper (n) a shoe that you wear indoors or for dancing.

stepmother (n) when your father marries again, his new wife is your stepmother.

suddenly (adv) very quickly.

touch (v) when you touch something, you put your fingers or your hand on it. You can also touch one thing with another thing.

wand (n) a special kind of stick that fairies use to do magic.

whisper (v) when you say something very, very quietly, you whisper.

wide (adj) the opposite of narrow.

you shall go to the ball When Cinderella's godmother says this, she means "I am going to make this happen".

Answers

What happened when?

C, E, F, D, A, B

What do they want?

A – Imelda   B – Griselda
C – Cinderella   D – the Prince
E – the Fairy Godmother

What do they think?
How do they feel?

1. sad   2. excited
3. frightened 4. important

You shall go to the ball

1. B
2. C
3. A

What happened next?

1. A
2. B
3. A

You can find information about other Usborne English Readers here:
usborneenglishreaders.com

Designed by Melissa Gandhi
Series designer: Laura Nelson Norris
Edited by Mairi Mackinnon
Digital imaging: John Russell

Page 24: picture of Charles Perrault © White Images/Scala, Florence.

First published in 2017 by Usborne Publishing Ltd.,
Usborne House, 83-85 Saffron Hill, London EC1N 8RT, England.
usborne.com Copyright © 2017 Usborne Publishing Ltd.